For Kay Harrison

My World of Words copyright © Frances Lincoln Limited 1995
Text copyright © Debbie MacKinnon 1995
Photographs copyright © Frances Lincoln Limited 1995
Postcard illustration copyright © Frané Lessac 1990

First published in Great Britain in 1995 by
Frances Lincoln Limited, 4 Torriano Mews
Torriano Avenue, London NW5 2RZ

First paperback edition 1996

British Library Cataloguing in Publication Data
available on request

ISBN 0-7112-0982-0 hardback
ISBN 0-7112-0983-9 paperback

Printed in Hong Kong

1 3 5 7 9 8 6 4 2

My World of Words

Debbie MacKinnon
Photographed by
Geoff Dann

Introduced by Betty Root

FRANCES LINCOLN

About this book

Children respond to words, sounds and conversation almost as soon as they are born. Understanding words helps them to communicate with others and to make sense of the world around them. From an early age they love to know the names of everything they see and use.

My World of Words has been carefully and imaginatively designed to encourage children to extend their knowledge of words. The pictures have been grouped into categories so that young children will gain an understanding of the basic concepts of *colour, number* and *shape* – as well as exploring ideas of size and function under the headings of *opposites* and *noises*.

In their first few years children are constantly learning a wide range of skills. Parents play a vital, supportive role in these important developmental processes. Sharing this book with a grown-up will enable children to make links between what they know and what they need to express. A child may know that a favourite toy is called *a ball*, but further discussion will establish that is is a *blue* ball, a *round* ball, a *big* ball, and that there is *one* ball.

Parents can explain that some of the *five leaves* have five points, the *five gloves* have five fingers, the *two feet* could fit into the *two shoes* shown below them. Ideas of colour, size and so on can be discussed throughout: for example, of the *four toothbrushes*, which one is the biggest, and what colours are they? Thus by observing and talking about pictures, the child's language is extended and enriched.

My World of Words can be used to great advantage at many levels, including simple identification of objects, discussion of concepts and development of early reading skills. It can be shared within a family and returned to again and again.

- the size is right for small children
- the photographs are easily identified
- the objects shown are familiar
- the print is clear
- the pictures are specially chosen to illustrate five important concepts
- the match of words and pictures encourages reading

Sharing **My World of Words** with children ensures that they see words as fascinating and useful. Learning from this book is exciting, rewarding and fun.

Betty Root

Contents

Colours

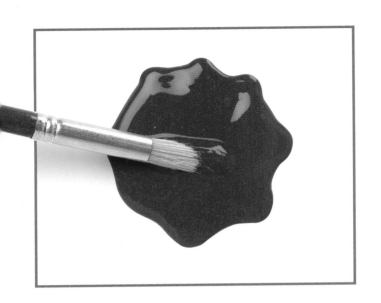

red paint

red strawberry

red tomato

red boots

blue paint

blue bucket

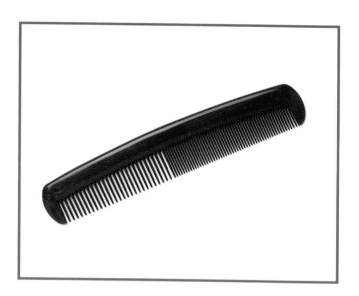

blue comb

blue jeans

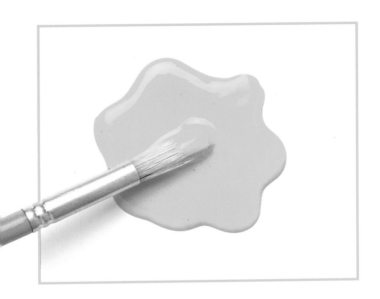

yellow paint

yellow duck

yellow flower

yellow banana

green paint

green frog

green apple

green lettuce

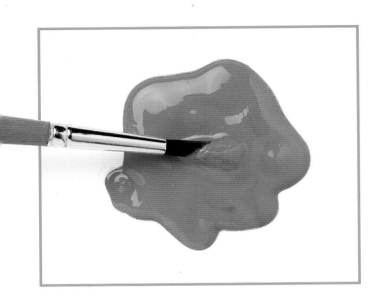

orange paint

orange

orange carrots

orange socks

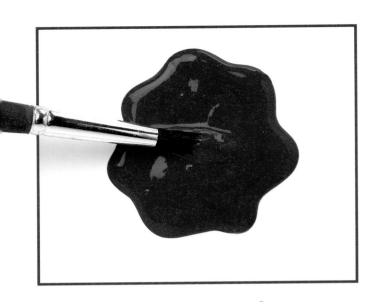

purple paint

purple umbrella

purple bow

purple sweatshirt

black paint

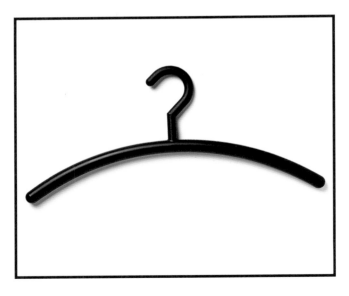

black hanger

black frying pan

black kitten

white paint

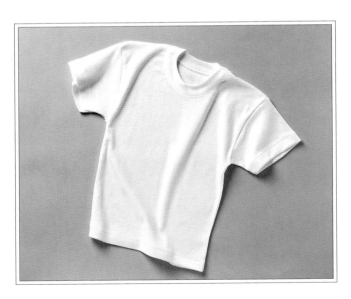

white T-shirt

white cotton wool

white hairbrush

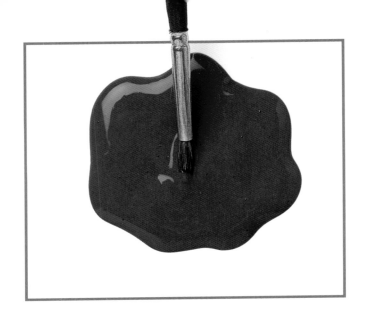

brown paint

brown chocolate

brown rabbit

brown bowl

pink paint

pink tights

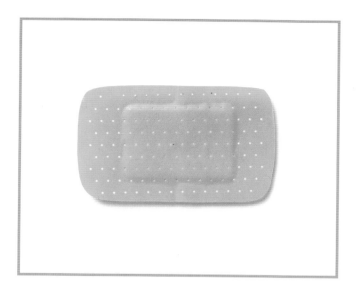

pink plaster

pink handbag

Look at all the coloured pens!
How many colours can you
see in the rainbow?

Numbers

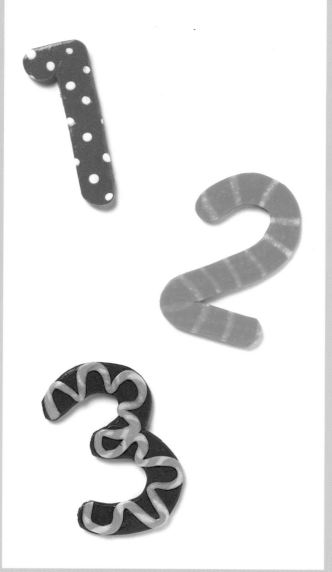

one

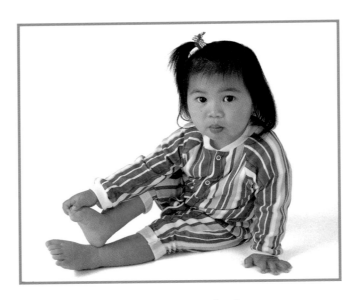

one girl

one cup

one chair

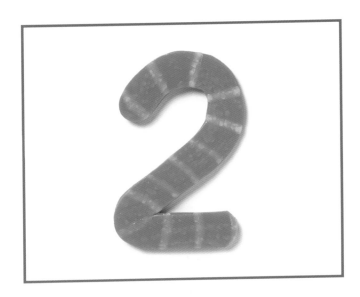

two

two twins

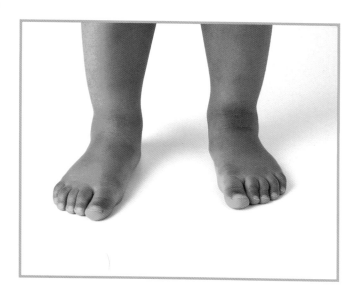

two feet

two shoes

three

three dolls

three cherries

three forks

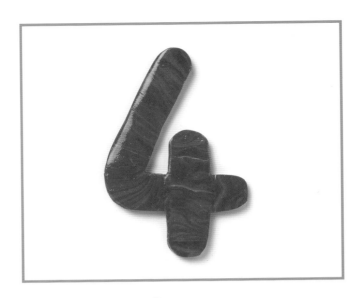

four

four marbles

four toothbrushes

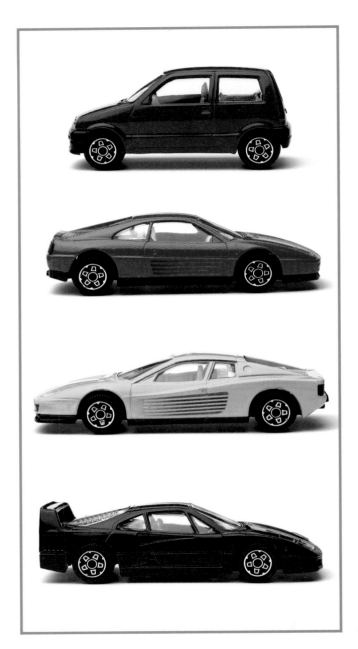

four cars

five

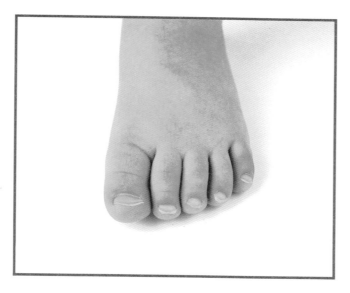

five toes

five leaves

five gloves

six

six raisins

six fish

six diggers

47

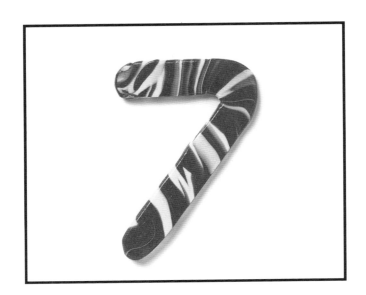

seven

seven ladybirds

seven boats

seven balls

eight

eight pebbles

eight spoons

eight shells

nine

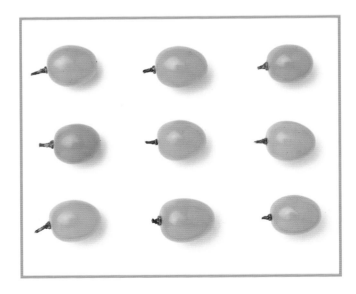

nine grapes

nine bricks

nine balloons

ten

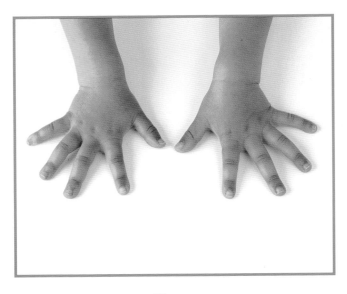

ten fingers

ten crayons

ten dinosaurs

eleven

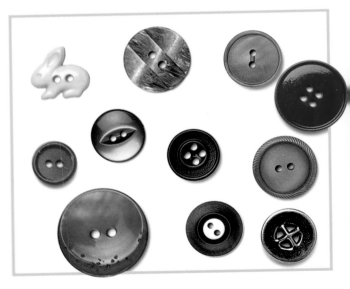

eleven buttons

twelve

twelve sweets

Look at all the toys!
Can you count 3 balls,
2 diggers and 1 doll?

Shapes

round

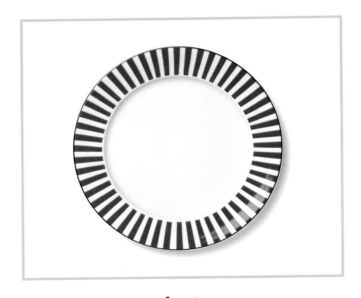

plate

ball

cake

square

soft block

jigsaw puzzle

photograph

triangle

sandwich

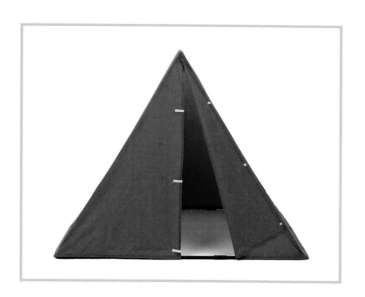

tent

slice of pizza

rectangle

envelope

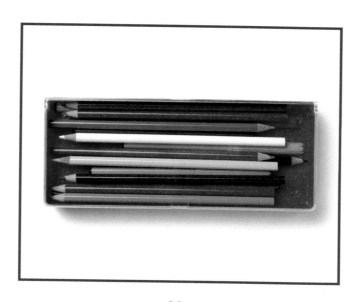

pencil case

postcard

oval

egg

sponge

pine cone

diamond

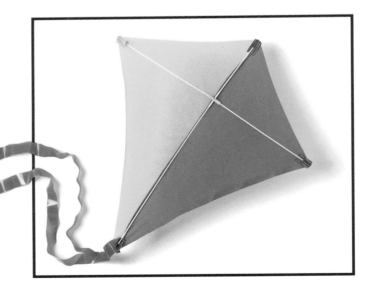

kite

earrings

chocolates

ring

doughnut

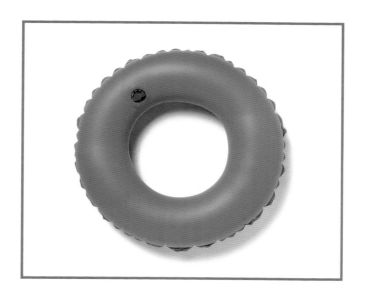

rubber ring

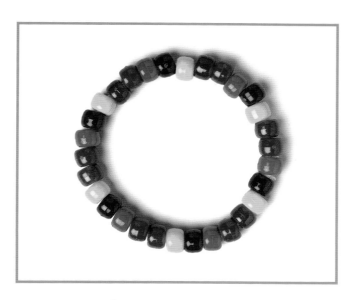

bracelet

heart

biscuit

locket

soap

star

magic wand

starfish

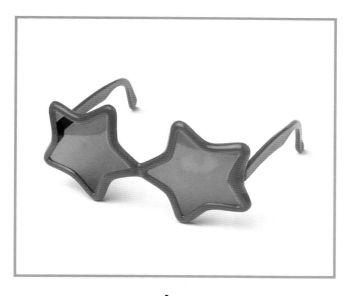

sunglasses

semicircle

hat

watermelon

purse

Look at all the shapes
in this clown!
What shapes can you see?

Opposites

big present

little present

big baby

little baby

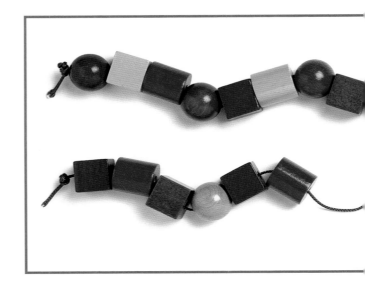

short string of beads

short train

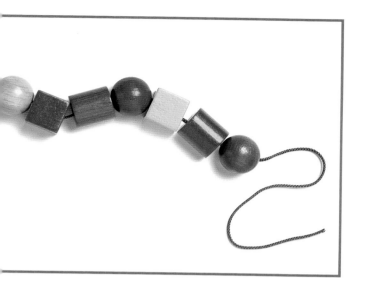

long string of beads

long train

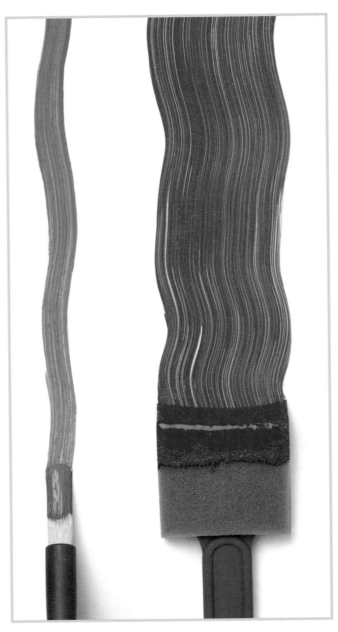

thin line   thick line

thin book

thick book

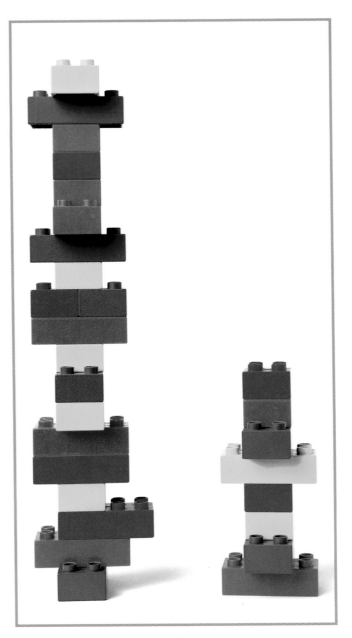

tall tower   small towe

small boy   tall girl

clean

dirty

front

back

full beaker

empty beaker

full basket

empty basket

old

young

open

closed

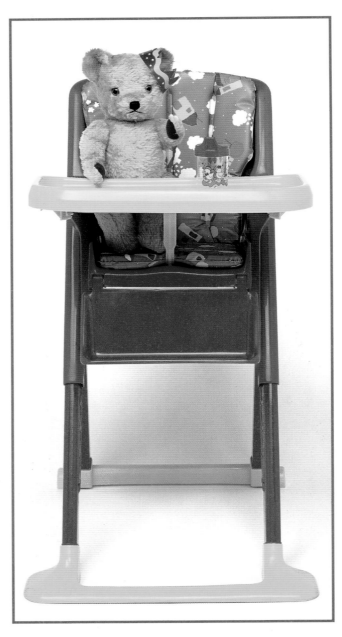

highchair

low chair

asleep

awake

happy

sad

Look at all the teddy bears!
Which one is the biggest?
Which is the littlest bear?

Noises

woof woof

meow

squawk

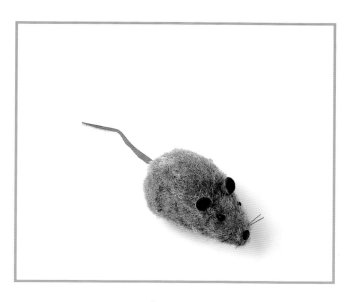

squeak squeak

moooo

oink oink

baa baa

neigh

hissss

terump-teraa

roarrr

chi-chi-chi

cluck cluck

quack quack

cheep cheep

cock-a-doodle-doo!

toot toot

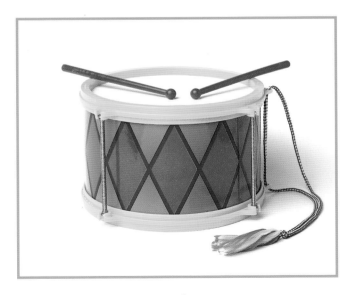

bang bang

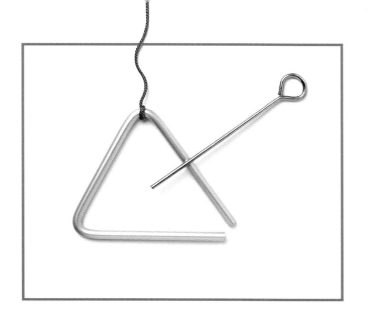

ting!

ding-a-ling

tick-tock

brring-brring

varooom

click

Look at all the noisy things.
Which one makes the
loudest noise?

Index